HALL OF FAME
BASEBALL

TRIVIA

By Steve Fiorentine

RED-LETTER PRESS, INC.
Saddle River, New Jersey

Hall of Fame Baseball Trivia

Copyright ©2015 Red-Letter Press, Inc.
ISBN-10: 1-60387-078-4
ISBN-13: 978-1-60387-078-8

Red-Letter Press, Inc.
P.O. Box 393, Saddle River, NJ 07458
www.Red-LetterPress.com
info@Red-LetterPress.com

ACKNOWLEDGMENTS

COVER ART:
Andrew Towl

•

BOOK DESIGN & TYPOGRAPHY:
Jeff Kreismer

•

EDITORIAL:
Jack Kreismer

•

RESEARCH AND DEVELOPMENT:
Kobus Reyneke

HALL OF FAME
BASEBALL

TRIVIA

Hall of Fame Baseball Trivia

First Pitch

1. By picking up the win against the Diamondbacks on April 30, 2002, who became the first pitcher in baseball history to defeat all 30 current major league teams?

2. With a game-winning home run in the bottom of the tenth inning on April 14, 2011, Johnny Damon became the first player to hit walk off homers with five different MLB franchises. Name them.

3. Instant replay was used for the first time in MLB history on September 3, 2008, at Tropicana Field, when a home run off the bat of what player was upheld as fair after initially sailing over the left field foul pole?

4. Yankees manager Billy Martin penciled what pitcher into the starting lineup at designated hitter on June 11, 1988, making him the first hurler ever to start at DH?

5. By entering Game 3 of the 2014 World Series, who became the first player to appear in both the College World Series and Fall Classic during the same season?

Hall of Fame Baseball Trivia

ANSWERS

1. Al Leiter

2. The Kansas City Royals, Boston Red Sox,
New York Yankees, Detroit Tigers and Tampa Bay Rays

3. Alex Rodriguez

4. Rick Rhoden

5. Brandon Finnegan, who pitched for both Texas
Christian University and the Royals in 2014

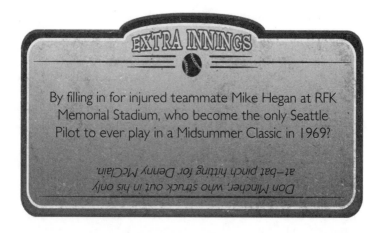

By filling in for injured teammate Mike Hegan at RFK
Memorial Stadium, who become the only Seattle
Pilot to ever play in a Midsummer Classic in 1969?

Don Mincher, who struck out in his only
at-bat pinch hitting for Denny McClain.

Hall of Fame Baseball Trivia

OPENING DAY

1. On April 16, 1940, Bob Feller tossed the only Opening Day no-hitter in baseball history. However, Feller's "No-No" isn't the earliest in terms of calendar date. Whose was?

2. Three players have hit three home runs in a single game on Opening Day: George Bell, Tuffy Rhodes and Dmitri Young. Which of the three hit the most career MLB homers?

3. On April 9, 1990, what Houston Astros player came to the plate six times and set a record by becoming the first player to be hit by three pitches on Opening Day?

4. Chicago White Sox catcher Ron Karkovice started the season on a sour note in 1996 by going 0-for-5 at the plate against the Seattle Mariners on Opening Day. All five of Karkovice's outs came by what variety?

5. April 4, 1999, marked the first regular season game played outside of North America when the San Diego Padres played host to the Colorado Rockies in what city?

Hall of Fame Baseball Trivia

ANSWERS

1. Hideo Nomo - He pitched a no-hitter for the Red Sox on April 4, 2001, the second game of the season.

2. Bell, owner of 265 career home runs

3. Glenn Davis

4. Strikeouts

5. Monterrey, Mexico

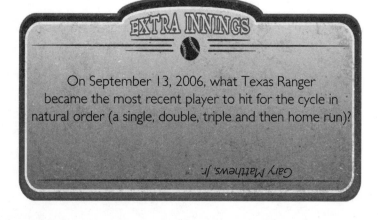

EXTRA INNINGS

On September 13, 2006, what Texas Ranger became the most recent player to hit for the cycle in natural order (a single, double, triple and then home run)?

Gary Matthews, Jr.

Hall of Fame Baseball Trivia

THE M&M BOYS

The answers to each of the
following all have the initials "M.M."

1. After being demoted to Triple-A earlier in
the season, this player established a new
Royals record by leading all players with five
home runs in the 2014 postseason. Who is he?

2. Born on July 6, 1992, this player hold the
record for the most multi-hit games before
turning 21 years of age, with 47. Who is he?

3. This pitcher's Game 1 start in the 2011
ALDS, in which he threw seven scoreless
innings against the Rangers, was just the
second start of his young career. Who is he?

4. By going yard in the second inning of Game 3 of
the 2010 World Series, this player hit the first Fall
Classic home run in Rangers history. Who is he?

5. Not even Randy Johnson accomplished
what this Mariners left-hander did on June
23, 2015, when he became the first Seattle
lefty to throw a complete game shutout with
10 strikeouts and no walks. Who is he?

Hall of Fame Baseball Trivia

ANSWERS

1. Mike Moustakas

2. Manny Machado

3. Matt Moore

4. Mitch Moreland

5. Mike Montgomery

In 2015, the Los Angeles Dodgers became the
first team in history to have two different
pitchers strike out four batters in one inning on
consecutive nights. Name the two pitchers.

Kenley Jansen and Sergio Santos

THE ONE AND ONLY

1. By wearing No. 17 for the White Sox, who became the only player in baseball history to wear both the month and date of his birth on the back of his jersey?

2. On July 17, 1990, the Minnesota Twins became the only team in baseball history to turn two triple plays in the same game, with each instance being scored 5-4-3. What trio of infielders was responsible for turning both plays?

3. Who is the only pitcher in baseball history to win the clinching game of two different World Series for two different teams?

4. Often considered one of the hardest single-game feats in baseball, just 16 players have hit four home runs in one game. Who is the only player to do so while making just four plate appearances?

5. Who is the only man man to play 165 games in a single season?

Everybody has something to prove each year. Everybody has a responsibility in this game. Even the batboy. -David Ortiz

Hall of Fame Baseball Trivia

ANSWERS

1. Carlos May, who was born on May 17, 1948

2. Gary Gaetti, Al Newman and Kent Hrbek

3. John Lackey, who won Game 7 of the 2002 World Series for the Anaheim Angels and Game 6 of the 2013 World Series for the Red Sox

4. Carlos Delgado, on September 25, 2003

5. Maury Wills, who played three extra games in 1962 thanks to the Dodgers three-game tie-breaker series against the San Francisco Giants

Of the top four career home run hitters whose last name begins with the letter "T", is Frank Thomas first, second, third or fourth on the list?

He's first and fourth – Hall of Famer Frank Thomas hit 521 homers. Another Frank Thomas, a career National Leaguer in the 1950s and '60s, had 286.

MANAGER MANIA

1. Only three former players have made their managerial debut after being inducted into the National Baseball Hall of Fame. Can you name the trio of skippers?

2. In need of a change, the Cleveland Indians and Detroit Tigers swapped managers midseason on August 3, 1960. Can you name the two skippers traded for each other?

3. With 1,902 victories as a manager under his belt, who is the winningest skipper to never win a pennant?

4. On November 5, 1997, what skipper notoriously resigned from his post on the same day he was named the American League's Manager of the Year?

5. The 1934 World Series between the St. Louis Cardinals and Detroit Tigers marked the last time two teams led by player-managers squared off in the Fall Classic. Who were the two multi-taskers?

After I hit a home run I had a habit of running the bases with my head down. I figured the pitcher already felt bad enough without me showing him up rounding the bases. -Mickey Mantle

Hall of Fame Baseball Trivia

ANSWERS

1. Ted Williams, Ryne Sandberg and Paul Molitor

2. The Tribe sent Joe Gordon to Detroit for Jimmy Dykes.

3. Gene Mauch

4. Davey Johnson, who resigned as
skipper of the Baltimore Orioles

5. Frankie Frisch and Mickey Cochrane

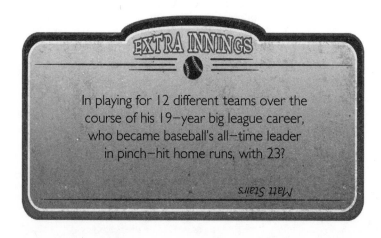

In playing for 12 different teams over the
course of his 19-year big league career,
who became baseball's all-time leader
in pinch-hit home runs, with 23?

Matt Stairs

COOPERSTOWN QUERIES

1. The National Baseball Hall of Fame opened in 1939, the same year in which three future Hall of Famers were born. Do you know who they are?

2. In 1992, Tom Seaver was elected to the National Baseball Hall of Fame with the largest voting percentage ever at 98.84%. Who found his way into Cooperstown with the lowest percentage?

3. Who is the only Hall of Famer to have played more than half of his career games at designated hitter?

4. Which cap logo is depicted on Catfish Hunter's Hall of Fame plaque: the Athletics or Yankees?

5. With their inductions to Cooperstown in 2015, Craig Biggio and Randy Johnson became the first players to represent the Astros and Diamondbacks on their plaques, leaving five current teams unrepresented. Can you name them?

Baseball, it is said, is only a game. True. And the Grand Canyon is only a hole in Arizona.
-George F. Will

Hall of Fame Baseball Trivia

ANSWERS

1. Lou Brock, Phil Niekro and Carl Yastrzemski

2. Al Simmons, who garnered 75.38 percent of the vote

3. Frank Thomas, who played 1,310
games at DH and 971 at first base

4. Neither - Hunter is one of nine players in
Cooperstown whose plaque does not feature a cap logo.

5. The Colorado Rockies, Miami Marlins, Seattle Mariners,
Tampa Bay Rays and Washington Nationals
(However, Gary Carter and Andre Dawson are
both depicted wearing Montreal Expos caps.)

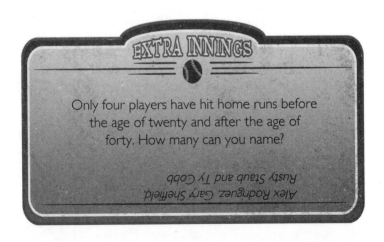

EXTRA INNINGS

Only four players have hit home runs before
the age of twenty and after the age of
forty. How many can you name?

Alex Rodriguez, Gary Sheffield,
Rusty Staub and Ty Cobb

A GLOBAL GAME

1. On June 5, 2002, who became the first man to hit two major league grand slams on two different continents?

2. What pitcher is the only Australian-born player to win the World Series?

3. What Hall of Famer served as the manager for Brazil during the 2013 World Baseball Classic?

4. In 2013, this former major leaguer from Curacao tackled Japan's longstanding single-season home run record set by Sadaharu Oh in 1964 by swatting 60 home runs for the Tokyo Yakult Swallows. Do you know who he is?

5. Prior to the 2015 season, the Red Sox shattered the record for the largest signing bonus ever given to an international amateur player when they handed what 19-year-old Cuban a $31.5 million bonus?

I knew when my career was over. In 1965 my baseball card came out with no picture. -Bob Uecker

Hall of Fame Baseball Trivia

ANSWERS

1. Benny Agbayani, who previously hit a grand slam during the Mets Opening Day game in 2000 against the Chicago Cubs in Japan

2. Graeme Lloyd, who was a part of two championship teams with the Yankees in 1996 and 1998

3. Barry Larkin

4. Wladimir Balentein

5. Yoan Moncada

EXTRA INNINGS

Who played Jackie Robinson in
The Jackie Robinson Story?

You weren't thinking of the 2013 movie 42, in
which Chadwick Boseman played Robinson, were
you? Jackie played himself in the 1950 biopic.

NICKNAMES

Match each player to his alternate alias.

1. Rich Garces   a. The Crime Dog

2. Travis Hafner   b. El Guapo

3. Hideki Matsui   c. Godzilla

4. Nyjer Morgan   d. Tony Plush

5. Fred McGriff   e. Pronk

**The difference between the old ballplayer and the
new ballplayer is the jersey. The old ballplayer
cared about the name on the front. The new
ballplayer cares about the name on the back.
-Steve Garvey**

ANSWERS

1. b

2. e

3. c

4. d

5. a

EXTRA INNINGS

In his final season in Japan, Masahiro Tanaka went 24–0 for the Tohoku Rakuten Golden Eagles. In 2014, he went 6–0 in his first eight starts for the Yankees. On May 20, what team handed Tanaka his first loss since August 19, 2012?

The Chicago Cubs, who defeated New York 6–1

ODD MAN OUT

1. Which of the Molina brothers did not win a Gold Glove at catcher: Bengie, Jose or Yadier?

2. Which of the following AL Cy Young winners was not a lefty: Pat Hentgen, Johan Santana or Barry Zito?

3. Which of the following pitchers never won 20 games in a single season: Chuck Finley, Mike Mussina or David Wells?

4. Which of the following sluggers never won a Home Run Derby: Garrett Anderson, Eric Davis or Richie Sexson?

5. Which of the following pitchers did not have a signature sneaker with Nike: Kenny Lofton, Hideo Nomo or Mo Vaughn?

I believe in the Church of Baseball. I tried all the major religions and most of the minor ones. I've worshipped Buddha, Allah, Brahma, Vishnu, Siva, trees, mushrooms and Isadora Duncan. I know things. For instance, there are 108 beads in a Catholic rosary and there are 108 stitches in a baseball. When I learned that, I gave Jesus a chance. -Ron Shelton, *Bull Durham*, 1988

Hall of Fame Baseball Trivia

ANSWERS

1. Jose

2. Hentgen

3. Finley

4. Sexson

5. Vaughn

EXTRA INNINGS

What former National League MVP was the
first player to hit a home run in three
different no–hitters (1991, '94 and '96)?

*Terry Pendleton, who hit a home run backing teammates Al
Leiter in 1996, Kent Mercker in 1994, and three different
Braves pitchers as part of a combined "No–No" in 1991*

Hall of Fame Baseball Trivia

THE AGONY OF DEFEAT

1. In their inaugural 1962 season, the New York Mets recorded a major league record 120 losses. How many games out of first place did they finish behind the pennant-winning Giants?

a) 20.5   b) 40.5   c) 60.5

2. Starting in 1993, the Pirates began a streak of how many consecutive losing seasons, establishing a North American professional sports record for futility?

3. The 2003 Tigers rotation is the only one in history to feature the major's top three league leaders in losses. Can you name any of them?

4. On July 15, 2007, what team became the first in professional sports to lose 10,000 games? (Hint: Adam Eaton was the losing pitcher in a 10-2 loss to the Cardinals.)

5. What pitcher lost the most games in the history of Major League Baseball?

Hall of Fame Baseball Trivia

ANSWERS

1. C

2. 20

3. Mike Maroth (9-21), Jeremy Bonderman (6-19)
and Nate Cornejo (6-17)

4. Philadelphia Phillies

5. Cy Young, who, of course, also won
the most with a 511-316 record

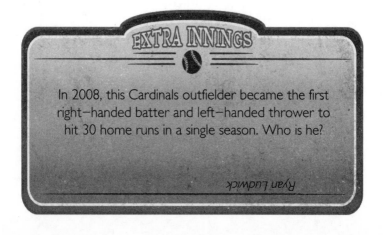

EXTRA INNINGS

In 2008, this Cardinals outfielder became the first
right–handed batter and left–handed thrower to
hit 30 home runs in a single season. Who is he?

Ryan Ludwick

SECOND GUESSING

1. On October 6, 2010, Roy Halladay tossed the second no-hitter in playoff history. Halladay's gem would have also been the second postseason perfect game if not for the walk drawn by what Reds batter?

2. Roger Clemens tied his own MLB record for strikeouts when he fanned 20 batters for a second time on September 18, 1996, against the Tigers. What Detroit shortstop picked up a "Golden Sombrero" by striking out four times against "The Rocket?"

3. Barry Bonds sits atop the all-time intentional walks list with 688 career free passes. Who is a distant second with 293?

4. The New York Yankees have the most World Series appearances, playing in 40 and winning 27. What team is second with 20 appearances?

5. During Rogers Hornsby's first Cardinals tenure from 1915-1926, the Redbirds did not wear uniform numbers. What number was Hornsby issued when he returned to St. Louis in 1933 for a brief second stint?

Hall of Fame Baseball Trivia

ANSWERS

1. Jay Bruce (Don Larsen of the Yankees threw a perfect game in Game 5 of the 1956 World Series against the Brooklyn Dodgers.)

2. Travis Fryman

3. Hank Aaron

4. The San Francisco Giants - They've played in 20 Fall Classics and have an 8-12 record.

5. No. 4

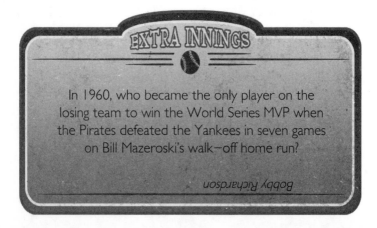

EXTRA INNINGS

In 1960, who became the only player on the losing team to win the World Series MVP when the Pirates defeated the Yankees in seven games on Bill Mazeroski's walk–off home run?

Bobby Richardson

HIS PLAYING DAYS ARE NUMBERED

1. Luis Aparicio's No. 11 was retired by the White Sox on August 14, 1984. However, Chicago briefly took the number out of retirement from 2010-11 so what fellow Venezuelan shortstop could wear it?

2. When the Expos moved to D.C. and became the Nationals, the franchise re-circulated the four numbers retired during the team's time in Montreal. At what Montreal venue is there still a banner honoring the Expos four retired numbers?

3. On August 23, 2015, the Yankees retired the No. 46 in Andy Pettitte's honor. How many other teams across baseball have retired #46?

4. Of the ten numbers the Dodgers have retired, only one of them belongs to a player who is not in the National Baseball Hall of Fame. Who is he?

5. Who is the only player to have his number retired by the Mariners?

Hall of Fame Baseball Trivia

ANSWERS

1. Omar Vizquel

2. The Bell Centre, home of the NHL's Montreal Canadiens
(The retired numbers are 8 for Gary Carter, 10 for both
Andre Dawson and Rusty Staub, and 30 for Tim Raines.)

3. None

4. Jim Gilliam, whose No. 19 was
retired on October 10, 1978

5. Jackie Robinson, whose No. 42 was retired
league-wide in 1997 (Other than that, the
Mariners have never officially retired a number.)

EXTRA INNINGS

Who is the only man to play for the Boston
Braves, Milwaukee Braves and Atlanta Braves?

Eddie Mathews, who was with the
franchise from 1952–66

GOLD GLOVES

1. The Gold Glove Award was created in 1957 by what baseball manufacturer?

2. Who is the only player to have won a Gold Glove as both an infielder and an outfielder?

3. Since the award's inception in 2011, only one player besides Yadier Molina has won the National League's Platinum Glove Award, given to the best overall defender in each league. Who was it?

4. Pitcher Jim Kaat won 16 consecutive Gold Gloves from 1962-77. Name the three teams Kaat played for during his incredible run.

5. As Rangers teammates in 2000, this pitcher-catcher tandem earned Gold Gloves. After reuniting in Detroit, they'd do it twice more in 2004 and 2006 to become the only battery to earn the honor three times in the same season. Can you name the duo?

Aw, how could he lose the ball in the sun?
He's from Mexico. -Harry Caray

Hall of Fame Baseball Trivia

ANSWERS

1. Rawlings

2. Darin Erstad, who took home Gold Gloves
as both an outfielder and first baseman

3. Andrelton Simmons (2013)

4. The Twins, White Sox and Phillies

5. Kenny Rogers and Ivan Rodriguez

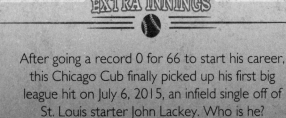

EXTRA INNINGS

After going a record 0 for 66 to start his career,
this Chicago Cub finally picked up his first big
league hit on July 6, 2015, an infield single off of
St. Louis starter John Lackey. Who is he?

Jon Lester

BEAT THE STREAK

1. On April 5, 1989, what Red knocked in Barry Larkin with an RBI single in the bottom of the first against the Dodgers to put an end to Orel Hershiser's 59 consecutive scoreless innings streak?

2. Who won the Gold Glove Award for American League third basemen in 1976, putting an end to Brooks Robinson's streak of 16 consecutive awards at the hot corner?

3. Joe DiMaggio's famed 56-game hitting streak came to a close on July 17, 1941, against the Indians. What two Cleveland pitchers held the Yankee Clipper hitless for the day?

4. Eric Gagne's 84 consecutive saves streak came to an end on July 5, 2004, when he coughed up a 5-3 Dodgers ninth inning lead to what team?

5. Over the course of eight games, from July 22 to August 28, 2014, Giants pitcher Yusmeiro Petit pitched 15.1 consecutive perfect innings. What Rockies pitcher put an end to Petit's perfect streak by hitting a double?

Hall of Fame Baseball Trivia

ANSWERS

1. Todd Benzinger

2. Aurelio Rodriguez

3. Al Smith and Jim Bagby

4. The Diamondbacks (Arizona handed Gagne his last blown save on August 26, 2002, before his streak started.)

5. Jordan Lyles

When the Cubs visited the Phillies on September 29, 1986, it marked the first time in major league history that two brothers faced each other as rookie starting pitchers. Who were they?

Greg and Mike Maddux — The Cubs beat the Phillies 8–3, with Greg picking up the victory.

MASCOTS

1. What is the fictional birthplace of the Phillie Phanatic?

2. During the fourth inning of every home game, the Nationals hold a live-action Presidents Race in which caricatures of five different U.S. Presidents race around the field. Who is the only President represented in the races that's not featured on Mt. Rushmore?

3. After a 12-year hiatus, Orbit was reintroduced as the Astros official mascot prior to the 2013 season. Who served as Houston's mascot from 2000-12 during Orbit's absence?

4. In 2003, who became the only person in Mets history to wear No. 00 besides Mr. Met?

5. What Pirates player was suspended three games in 2003 for hitting the Brewers Italian Sausage mascot with a bat during the sixth inning Sausage Race?

The last time the Cubs won a World Series was 1908. The last time they were in one was 1945. Hey, any team can have a bad century. -Former Cubs manager Tom Trebelhorn

Hall of Fame Baseball Trivia

ANSWERS

1. The Galapagos Islands

2. William Howard Taft

3. Junction Jack

4. Tony Clark, who switched to No. 52 later
in the season due to backlash from fans

5. Randall Simon

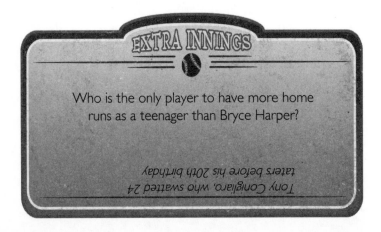

EXTRA INNINGS

Who is the only player to have more home
runs as a teenager than Bryce Harper?

Tony Conigliaro, who swatted 24
taters before his 20th birthday

TWO OF A KIND

1. Who are the only two players in baseball history to win the Rookie of the Year, MVP and Cy Young awards in their careers?

2. Who are the only two switch-hitters in the 3,000 hits club?

3. Only two pitchers in baseball history have struck out ten or more batters in eight consecutive starts. Do you know who they are?

4. Due to two tie games, the Cubs played two extra games during the 1965 season. What two players played in all 164 games that year?

5. From 1977-95, this double play combo played 1,918 games together, making them the longest continuous double play combo in history. Can you name them?

During my 18 years I came to bat almost 10,000 times. I struck out about 1,700 times and walked maybe 1,800 times. You figure a ballplayer will average about 500 at bats a season. That means I played seven years without ever hitting the ball. -Mickey Mantle

Hall of Fame Baseball Trivia

ANSWERS

1. Don Newcombe and Justin Verlander

2. Eddie Murray and Pete Rose

3. Pedro Martinez in 1999 and Chris Sale in 2015

4. Ron Santo and Billy Williams

5. Alan Trammell and Lou Whitaker

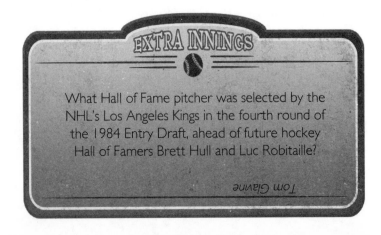

EXTRA INNINGS

What Hall of Fame pitcher was selected by the NHL's Los Angeles Kings in the fourth round of the 1984 Entry Draft, ahead of future hockey Hall of Famers Brett Hull and Luc Robitaille?

Tom Glavine

Hall of Fame Baseball Trivia

SIGNAL CALLERS

The following NFL quarterbacks were all
drafted by major league franchises.
Match each QB to the team that picked him.

1. Troy Aikman   a. Cubs

2. Tom Brady   b. Expos

3. John Elway   c. Mets

4. Colin Kaepernick   d. Padres

5. Johnny Manziel   e. Yankees

Hall of Fame Baseball Trivia

ANSWERS

1. c

2. b

3. e

4. a

5. d

EXTRA INNINGS

The Rays have been on the wrong side of a perfect game three different times. Name the three pitchers who achieved perfection against Tampa Bay.

Mark Buehrle (White Sox), Dallas Braden (A's) and Felix Hernandez (Mariners)

No-No's

1. Who is the only pitcher to have thrown his own no-hitter as a starter and contributed to a combined one as a reliever?

2. True or False? All-Star catchers Jason Varitek and Buster Posey share the record for the most no-hitters caught, with four.

3. Johan Santana's no-hitter for the Mets in 2012 left only one franchise without a "No-No" in its history. Do you know which one it is?

4. The most pitches ever thrown in a nine-inning no-hitter are 149, due largely in part to the eight walks surrendered by the pitcher. Do you know who threw it?

5. The first combined no-hitter took place on June 23, 1917, when Ernie Shore entered the game for the Red Sox in the first inning. What starting pitcher was ejected after walking the very first batter of the game?

I have discovered, in twenty years of moving around a ballpark, that the knowledge of the game is usually in inverse proportion to the price of the seats. -Bill Veeck

Hall of Fame Baseball Trivia

ANSWERS

1. Mike Witt, who threw a perfect game on September 30, 1984, and pitched two hitless innings in relief of Mark Langston on April 11, 1990

2. False - Varitek holds the mark by himself. While they've each played in four no-hitters, Posey started at first base for Tim Lincecum's "No-No" in 2014.

3. The Padres

4. Edwin Jackson, on June 25, 2010

5. Babe Ruth

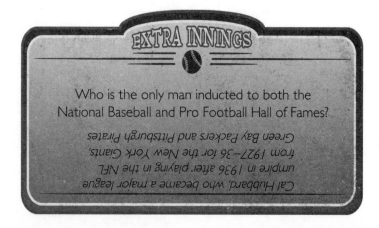

EXTRA INNINGS

Who is the only man inducted to both the National Baseball and Pro Football Hall of Fames?

Cal Hubbard, who became a major league umpire in 1936 after playing in the NFL from 1927–36 for the New York Giants, Green Bay Packers and Pittsburgh Pirates

THE 500 HOME RUN CLUB

1. Who is the only player to hit both his 499th and 500th career home runs in the same game?

2. Gary Sheffield's 500th career home run came on April 17, 2009. It's the only 500th home run to double as a player's first with a new team. What team was it?

3. Who leads all 500 home run club members with 28 postseason dingers?

4. On September 16, 2007, who became the only player to hit a walk off home run as his 500th career blast?

5. With just 4.4 percent of the BBWA's vote, who became the first 500 home run club member to be removed from the Hall of Fame ballot?

As I say, I never feel more at home in America than at a ball game, be it in a park or in sandlot. Beyond this I know not and dare not. -Robert Frost

Hall of Fame Baseball Trivia

ANSWERS

1. Albert Pujols

2. The Mets

3. Manny Ramirez - The 28 playoff home runs, of course, do not count towards Manny's 555 career long balls.

4. Jim Thome

5. Rafael Palmeiro

EXTRA INNINGS

Seven players have won both the LCS and World Series MVP awards in the same postseason. How many can you name?

Willie Stargell (1979), Darrell Porter (1982), Orel Hershiser (1988), Livan Hernandez (1997), Cole Hamels (2008), David Freese (2011) and Madison Bumgarner (2014)

THE MIDSUMMER CLASSIC

1. What player holds the record for most All-Star votes in a single-season, with 14.09 million?

2. Mike Trout was the first player in history to win back-to-back All-Star Game MVP Awards (2014 and '15). Only four others have won it twice. How many can you name?

3. The 2002 All-Star Game at Miller Park in Milwaukee ended in a 7-7 tie. How come?

4. After being voted to the NL All-Star squad by his fellow players in 2013, what pitcher was ruled ineligible to play following an interleague trade to the Athletics the day before selections?

5. With the awarding of the 2017 and 2018 All-Star Games to the Marlins and Nationals, respectively, there is only one major league franchise that has not been given the nod to host an All-Star Game. Which one?

Hall of Fame Baseball Trivia

ANSWERS

1. Josh Donaldson, who surpassed Josh Hamilton for the honor in 2015

2. Willie Mays (1963 and '68), Steve Garvey ('74 and '78), Gary Carter ('81 and '84), and Cal Ripken Jr. ('91 and 2001)

3. Both teams ran out of available pitchers.

4. Jeff Samardzija, who went 2-7 with a 2.83 ERA for the Cubs before the trade

5. The Rays

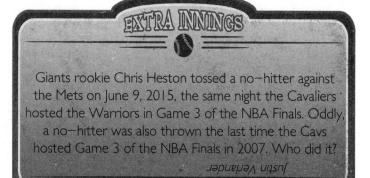

EXTRA INNINGS

Giants rookie Chris Heston tossed a no-hitter against the Mets on June 9, 2015, the same night the Cavaliers hosted the Warriors in Game 3 of the NBA Finals. Oddly, a no-hitter was also thrown the last time the Cavs hosted Game 3 of the NBA Finals in 2007. Who did it?

Justin Verlander

WELCOME TO THE SHOW

1. What player, way back in 1950, lays claim to being the oldest Rookie of the Year, edging out fellow 32-year-old winner Kazuhiro Sasaki by 33 days?

2. Game 1 of the 2006 World Series between the Cardinals and Tigers marked the first time two rookie pitchers faced each other in the opening game of the Fall Classic. Can you name them?

3. From 1992-96, the Dodgers pumped out five consecutive National League Rookie of the Year winners. How many can you name?

4. The 2008 All-Star Game at Yankee Stadium marked the only time two rookies were in the starting lineup for one team at the Midsummer Classic. Do you know who they are?

5. Fred Lynn and Ichiro Suzuki are the only two players to win Rookie of the Year and MVP honors in the same season. Mike Trout nearly joined them in 2012, but finished second in AL MVP balloting to whom?

Hall of Fame Baseball Trivia

ANSWERS

1. Sam Jethroe

2. Anthony Reyes and Justin Verlander

3. Eric Karros, Mike Piazza, Raul Mondesi,
Hideo Nomo and Todd Hollandsworth

4. Geovany Soto and Kosuke Fukudome, both of the Cubs

5. Miguel Cabrera

EXTRA INNINGS

In 1989, this Red Sox player became the
first Little Leaguer to be enshrined in the
Baseball Hall of Fame. Who is he?

Carl Yastrzemski

GREYBEARDS

1. By starting Game 4 of the 1929 World Series for the Philadelphia Athletics, who became the oldest player in postseason history at 46 years and 103 days old?

2. What 45-year-old shortstop retired following the 2012 season after having played in four different decades?

3. At age 42 in 2004, Roger Clemens became the oldest player to win a Cy Young by capturing his seventh and final award. Was Clemens' 2.98 ERA that season the lowest of his career?

4. On June 27, 2005, what Brave became the oldest player to a hit a grand slam in major league history?

5. In 2012, 49-year-old Jamie Moyer became the oldest pitcher in major league history to win a game as a member of what team?

The best possible thing in baseball is winning the World Series. The second best thing is losing the World Series. -Tommy Lasorda

Hall of Fame Baseball Trivia

ANSWERS

1. Jack Quinn

2. Omar Vizquel

3. No - The following year, at age 43,
"The Rocket" recorded a career best 1.87 ERA.

4. Julio Franco, at 46

5. Colorado Rockies

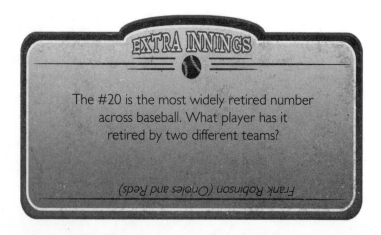

EXTRA INNINGS

The #20 is the most widely retired number
across baseball. What player has it
retired by two different teams?

Frank Robinson (Orioles and Reds)

DOWN ON THE FARM

1. Since the inception of the franchise in 1969, the Royals have had only one Triple-A affiliate. Can you name it?

2. In 2010, what Reds first round draft pick became the most recent pitcher to skip the minors entirely and go directly to the majors?

3. Every year since 1981, *Baseball America* has handed out its Minor League Player of the Year Award. Who are the only two prospects to win the award twice?

4. In 2012, the Yankees Triple-A affiliate spent its entire season on the road while their home ballpark was being renovated in what city?

5. In 2015, Major League Baseball experimented with what game innovation in the minor leagues in order to speed up the pace of play?

The way to make coaches think you're in shape in the spring is to get a tan. -Whitey Ford

Hall of Fame Baseball Trivia

ANSWERS

1. The Omaha Storm Chasers, formerly known as the Royals and Golden Spikes

2. Mike Leake

3. Gregg Jefferies and Andruw Jones

4. Moosic, Pennsylvania (part of the Scranton/Wilkes-Barre area)

5. A 20-second pitch clock

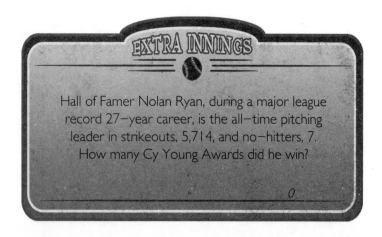

EXTRA INNINGS

Hall of Famer Nolan Ryan, during a major league record 27–year career, is the all–time pitching leader in strikeouts, 5,714, and no–hitters, 7. How many Cy Young Awards did he win?

0

STRANGE SIGHTS

Match each Hall of Famer to the team he last played for.

1. Yogi Berra	a. Athletics
2. Hank Greenberg	b. Indians
3. Harmon Killebrew	c. Pirates
4. Hal Newhouser	d. Mets
5. Billy Williams	e. Royals

ANSWERS

1. d

2. c

3. e

4. b

5. a

What are the only two teams to play in both
the American and National Leagues?

The Milwaukee Brewers and Houston Astros

TRIPLE PLAY

1. Only three men have hit a home run for their milestone 3,000th career hit. All played for the Yankees at one point. Who are they?

2. The 1981 World Series MVP was split between three different Dodgers players. Who are they?

3. Who are the only three players to win multiple Home Run Derby titles?

4. Three Canadian-born players have been named either AL or NL MVP. Can you name the trio?

5. Let's play *Jeopardy!* -- Harry Steinfeldt ... And the question is...

When I was a small boy growing up in Kansas, a friend of mine and I went fishing, and as we sat there in the warmth of a summer afternoon on a riverbank, we talked about what we wanted to do when we grew up. I told him that I wanted to be a real major-league baseball player, a genuine professional like Honus Wagner. My friend said that he'd like to be President of the United States. Neither of us got our wish. -Dwight David Eisenhower

Hall of Fame Baseball Trivia

ANSWERS

1. Wade Boggs, Derek Jeter and Alex Rodriguez

2. Ron Cey, Pedro Guerrero and Steve Yeager

3. Ken Griffey, Jr., Prince Fielder and Yoenis Cespedes

4. Larry Walker (1997), Justin Morneau (2006)
and Joey Votto (2010)

5. Who was the Cubs third baseman on the team that gained
fame for its "Tinker-to-Evers-to-Chance" double play trio?

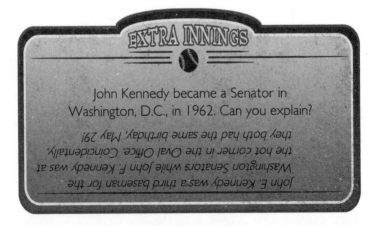

John Kennedy became a Senator in
Washington, D.C., in 1962. Can you explain?

John E. Kennedy was a third baseman for the
Washington Senators while John F. Kennedy was at
the hot corner in the Oval Office. Coincidentally,
they both had the same birthday, May 29!

TRADING PLACES

1. Following an April trade from the Mets to the Pirates in 2014, who became the only player in big league history to hit a grand slam for two different teams in the first month of the season?

2. Prior to the 1960 season, the Indians sent the previous year's home run champion to the Tigers for the defending batting champion. Can you name the two players?

3. The White Sox acquired future team captain Paul Konerko from the Reds in a straight-up trade for what outfielder who would later be sent to Seattle for Ken Griffey, Jr.?

4. On July 31, 2014, the Yankees and Red Sox made their first trade with each other since 1997. Who were the two players exchanged for one other?

5. On August 12, 1987, the Tigers acquired veteran pitcher Doyle Alexander from the Braves in exchange for a 20-year-old minor leaguer taken in the 22nd round of the 1985 First-Year Player Draft. Who?

Hall of Fame Baseball Trivia

ANSWERS

1. Ike Davis, who, oddly enough, hit both slams against the Cincinnati Reds

2. Rocky Colavito and Harvey Kuenn, respectively

3. Mike Cameron

4. Stephen Drew and Kelly Johnson

5. John Smoltz

EXTRA INNINGS

True or False? In their inaugural 1961 season, the Angels played at Wrigley Field.

True, but not the one in Chicago. Opened in 1925, L.A.'s Wrigley Field was home to the minor league version of the Angels until 1957 before the MLB club moved in for one season in 1961.

LEGENDS OF THE FALL

Match each of the following World Series MVP
winners who wore the same uniform numbers.

1. Josh Beckett a. Scott Brosius

2. David Freese b. Roberto Clemente

3. Ray Knight c. Jermaine Dye

4. Don Larsen d. David Eckstein

5. Edgar Renteria e. Frank Viola

Hall of Fame Baseball Trivia

ANSWERS

1. b (21)

2. c (23)

3. d (22)

4. a (18)

5. e (16)

EXTRA INNINGS

What five-time MLB All-Star was replaced at
quarterback by freshman Peyton Manning at the
University of Tennessee after suffering a knee
injury against Mississippi State in 1994?

Todd Helton

Hall of Fame Baseball Trivia

EITHER OR

1. Who had more home runs before the age of 25: Miguel Cabrera or Giancarlo Stanton?

2. Who had more wins in his Rookie of the Year-winning season: Mark Fidrych or Fernando Valenzuela?

3. Which co-MVP pitched more innings in the 2001 World Series: Randy Johnson or Curt Schilling?

4. Which closer recorded more saves in his World Series MVP-winning performance: John Wetteland in 1996 or Mariano Rivera in 1999?

5. Who had more hits in a Blue Jays uniform: Shannon Stewart or Vernon Wells?

Baseball is the only field of endeavor where a man can succeed three times out of ten and be considered a good performer. -Ted Williams

Hall of Fame Baseball Trivia

ANSWERS

1. Stanton, who slugged 154 homers
compared to Miggy's 138

2. Fidrych, whose 19 wins trumps Valenzuela's 13
(However, the 1981 strike-shortened season robbed
us of a few more "Fernandomania" starts.)

3. Schilling, who threw 21.1 innings opposed to
Johnson's 17.1 ("The Big Unit," however, had
three wins while Schilling had just one.)

4. Wetteland, who saved all four of the Yankees
victories against the Braves in the 1996 Fall Classic

5. Wells, who had 1,529 hits with Toronto

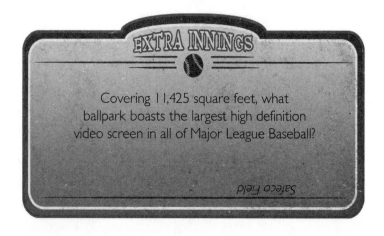

EXTRA INNINGS

Covering 11,425 square feet, what
ballpark boasts the largest high definition
video screen in all of Major League Baseball?

Safeco Field

THE FALL CLASSIC

1. In 1991, Lonnie Smith became the first player to appear in the World Series with four different teams. How many of them can you name?

2. Game 3 of the 1992 World Series in Toronto marked the first time the Fall Classic was played outside of the United States. Who hit the first World Series home run north of the border?

3. After not hitting a single home run during the entire regular season, what White Sox player hit a walk off home run in Game 2 of the 2005 World Series?

4. From 2007-09, this former American League Rookie of the Year made three consecutive trips to the World Series with three different AL East teams. Can you name him?

5. What Cardinal was picked off first base by Red Sox closer Koji Uehara in Game 4 of the 2013 World Series, marking the first time a Fall Classic game ended on a pickoff play?

Hall of Fame Baseball Trivia

ANSWERS

1. Phillies, Cardinals, Royals and Braves

2. Joe Carter

3. Scott Podsednik

4. Eric Hinske, who was on the Red Sox,
Rays and Yankees pennant-winning teams

5. Kolten Wong

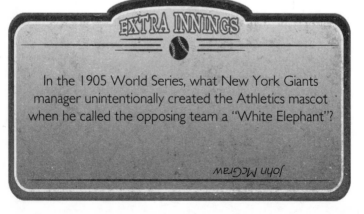

EXTRA INNINGS

In the 1905 World Series, what New York Giants
manager unintentionally created the Athletics mascot
when he called the opposing team a "White Elephant"?

John McGraw

THE BOTTOM LINE

1. The first contract in baseball history to eclipse $100 million came in December of 1998, when the Dodgers signed what starting pitcher to a seven-year, $105 million deal?

2. What player signed a 13-year, $325 million deal in November 2014, making it the richest contract in sports history?

3. When Robinson Cano signed his 10-year, $240 million contract with the Mariners, he did so with what rapper serving as his agent?

4. This pitcher, who tossed the final no-hitter of the 2012 season and the first no-hitter of the 2013 campaign, parlayed his success into a six-year, $105 million extension with the Reds. Do you know who he is?

5. When he was questioned about his 1930 contract of $80,000 being more than President Herbert Hoover's salary of $75,000, what player responded, "I had a better year than he did"?

**Has anybody ever satisfactorily explained why the bad hop is always the last one?
-Broadcaster Hank Greenwald**

Hall of Fame Baseball Trivia

ANSWERS

1. Kevin Brown

2. Giancarlo Stanton of the Miami Marlins

3. Jay Z

4. Homer Bailey

5. Babe Ruth

EXTRA INNINGS

There have been two pitchers who have struck out as many batters in a game as their ages. Can you name either of them?

Bob Feller, 17, and Kerry Wood, 20

ALL IN THE FAMILY

1. On June 1, 2012, the Dodgers established a new major league record when they had five sons of former major leaguers in their starting lineup. How many can you name?

2. Only one set of brothers can say they've each won a Cy Young Award. Do you know them? (Hint: One brother won in 1970 while the other won twice, in 1972 and '78.)

3. With two wins each, what brotherly pitching tandem was responsible for all four of the Cardinals victories against the Tigers in the 1934 World Series?

4. Bob and Ken Forsch are the only set of brothers to each throw a no-hitter at the big league level. Which one threw a second career no-hitter on September 26, 1983?

5. Who had more career home runs: Aaron or Bret Boone?

You spend a good piece of your life gripping a baseball and in the end it turns out that it was the other way around all the time. -Jim Bouton

Hall of Fame Baseball Trivia

ANSWERS

1. Tony Gwynn, Jr., Scott Van Slyke, Ivan De Jesus, Jr., Dee Gordon and Jerry Hairston, Jr.

2. Jim and Gaylord Perry

3. Jay Hanna Dean and Paul Dean, a.k.a. Dizzy and Daffy

4. Bob

5. Bret, who had 252

What Bill Veeck–inspired fashion statement and baseball first did the Chicago White Sox make on the hot summer afternoon of August 8, 1976?

They wore Bermuda shorts in the first game of a doubleheader against Kansas City.

Hall of Fame Baseball Trivia

THERE'S A DRAFT IN HERE

1. In 2011, the Pirates drafted Gerrit Cole out of UCLA with the first overall pick of the First-Year Player Draft. What team drafted Cole 28th overall in the first round of the 2008 draft but failed to sign him?

2. Which of the following players was drafted No. 1 overall straight out of high school: Kris Benson, Pat Burrell or Adrian Gonzalez?

3. Former No. 1 pick Josh Hamilton was plucked off the Devil Rays roster with the third overall pick in the 2006 Rule 5 Draft by what team who then flipped him to the Reds for $100,000?

4. In 1966, the Mets drafted catcher Steve Chilcott with the first overall pick in the First-Year Player Draft. What Hall of Famer was taken immediately after him at No. 2 by the Athletics?

5. After being drafted No. 1 overall by the Astros in 2014, Brady Aiken failed to sign a contract with the club before the July 18 deadline. What team drafted Aiken the following year with the 17th pick of the first round in 2015?

Hall of Fame Baseball Trivia

ANSWERS

1. Yankees

2. Gonzalez, who was taken out of Eastlake High School by the Marlins in 2000

3. Cubs

4. Reggie Jackson

5. Indians

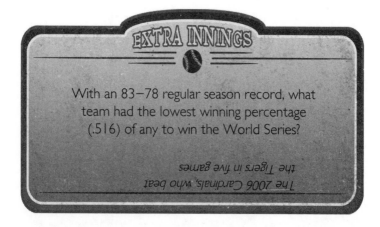

EXTRA INNINGS

With an 83–78 regular season record, what team had the lowest winning percentage (.516) of any to win the World Series?

The 2006 Cardinals, who beat the Tigers in five games

BRIEF STAYS

See if you can match each slugger to the
team that he played half a season or less
with before landing elsewhere.

1. Carlos Beltran

a. Athletics

2. Matt Holliday

b. Angels

3. Ken Griffey, Jr.

c. Giants

4. Mike Piazza

d. Marlins

5. Mark Teixeira

e. White Sox

Hall of Fame Baseball Trivia

ANSWERS

1. c

2. a

3. e

4. d

5. b

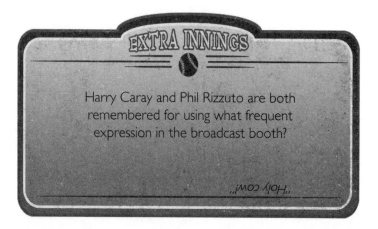

EXTRA INNINGS

Harry Caray and Phil Rizzuto are both remembered for using what frequent expression in the broadcast booth?

"Holy cow!"

THE RECORD BOOKS

1. What Dodgers great holds the single-season record for sacrifice flies, with 19?

2. Game-winning RBIs were kept briefly as an official stat from 1980-88. Given the time period, can you think of the all-time leader?

3. By winning the World Series MVP in 1989, Dave Stewart made up for the dubious pitching record he set the year before when he committed 16 of these.

4. In his 2007 National League MVP season, this player came to the plate more times than any other man in baseball history. Do you know who he is?

5. Perhaps best-known for his post-save "Bow and Arrow" celebration, this closer holds the record for the lowest single-season ERA by a relief pitcher, with a microscopic 0.60 mark.

You never know with those psychosomatic injuries. You have to take your time with them. -Jim Palmer

Hall of Fame Baseball Trivia

ANSWERS

1. Gil Hodges, in 1954

2. Keith Hernandez, who knocked in
129 runs with the Cardinals and Mets

3. Balks

4. Jimmy Rollins, who made 778 plate appearances

5. Fernando Rodney, who allowed just five earned
runs in 74.2 innings for the Rays in 2013

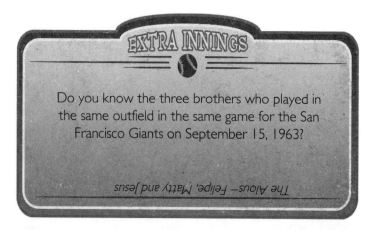

EXTRA INNINGS

Do you know the three brothers who played in
the same outfield in the same game for the San
Francisco Giants on September 15, 1963?

The Alous— Felipe, Matty and Jesus

Hall of Fame Baseball Trivia

STADIUM STUMPERS

1. For the first time in MLB history, on April 6, 2009, a player hit a leadoff homer in the first regular season game played in a new ballpark. Name the player and the park.

2. Built as the successor to Three Rivers Stadium, Pittsburgh's PNC Park sits along what river?

3. The Astrodome experienced its first-ever rained out game on June 15, 1976. How is this possible?

4. Name the four current major league ballparks featuring bullpens in playable foul territory.

5. Fenway Park is MLB's oldest stadium, built in 1912. Next is Wrigley Field, which opened in 1914. What's the third-oldest park?

I'd be willing to bet you, if I was a betting man, that I have never bet on baseball. -Pete Rose

Hall of Fame Baseball Trivia

ANSWERS

1. San Diego's Jody Gerut, at Citi Field

2. The Allegheny

3. Flooding in the Houston area prevented fans from getting to the ballpark, forcing the Astros to postpone the game.

4. AT&T Park (Giants), O.Co Coliseum (Athletics), Tropicana Field (Rays) and Wrigley Field (Cubs)

5. Dodger Stadium, opened in 1962

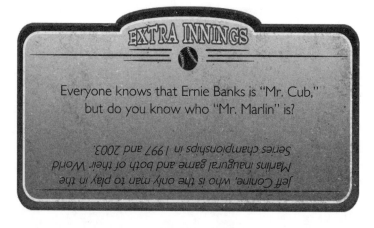

EXTRA INNINGS

Everyone knows that Ernie Banks is "Mr. Cub," but do you know who "Mr. Marlin" is?

Jeff Conine, who is the only man to play in the Marlins inaugural game and both of their World Series championships in 1997 and 2003.

Hall of Fame Baseball Trivia

WHO AM I?

1. I am the longest tenured play-by-play broadcaster of any single team in sports history.

2. Two Heisman Trophy winners have been big league baseball players. One is Vic Janowics. The other is me.

3. I played in 14 World Series games, seven in 1960 and seven in 1971, and hit safely in every one of them. Hint: In my career, I had exactly 3,000 hits.

4. I have the same amount of lifetime hits at the plate as I do victories on the mound, which happens to be the most of any left-handed pitcher in history.

5. On September 5, 2007, I hit the final home run of my career off of Colorado Rockies righthander Ubaldo Jiminez.

McCovey swings and misses, and it's fouled back. -Broadcaster Jerry Coleman

Hall of Fame Baseball Trivia

ANSWERS

1. Vin Scully, with the Dodgers since 1950

2. Bo Jackson

3. Roberto Clemente

4. Warren Spahn (363 hits and wins)

5. Barry Bonds (762 homers)

EXTRA INNINGS

If you were to list every active major leaguer
in alphabetical order, what Mariners catcher,
who won the Golden Spikes Award at the
University of Florida in 2012, would be last?

Mike Zunino

Closing Time

1. In 2008, Francisco Rodriguez set the single-season saves record by converting 62 successfully. How many saves did K-Rod blow in his historic season?

a) 7   b) 11   c) 13

2. Only two pitchers have recorded more than 600 career saves. Can you name them?

3. Hall of Fame relievers Rollie Fingers and Dennis Eckersley each won MVP awards in the American League. Who is the only pitcher to win the National League MVP out of the bullpen?

4. What three pitchers have led their league in saves and also thrown a no-hitter?

5. Madison Bumgarner's Game 7 save in the 2014 World Series was the longest save in Fall Classic history. How many innings did MadBum pitch in the record-setting performance?

I don't want to play golf. When I hit a ball, I want someone else to go chase it. -Rogers Hornsby

Hall of Fame Baseball Trivia

ANSWERS

1. A - giving him an 89.9 percent
conversion rate on the year

2. Mariano Rivera (652) and Trevor Hoffman (601)

3. Jim Konstanty, in 1950

4. Dave Righetti, Dennis Eckersley and Derek Lowe

5. Five

EXTRA INNINGS

Of all the members in the 500 Home Run Club,
there's only one player who homered in the
final at–bat of his career. Name him.

Ted Williams, #521